Moving Day

Meredith Costain

Illustrated by Wendy Straw

We are moving.

I woke up early.

I packed my books and toys in a big box.

I rolled up my blankets and quilt,

and put them in another box.

I helped my mother wrap up the plates and cups.

I wrapped them in newspaper

and put them in a box.

I nearly packed Salty,

but she jumped out of the box just in time.

A huge truck came
and parked at the front
of our house.
I helped carry out some of the boxes.
There were so many boxes.

When all the boxes were packed into the truck,
my mother and father and I walked
through the house.
We said good-bye to my room.
We said good-bye to every room.
I like this house.
I am going to miss it.

I am going to miss Aaron, too.

Aaron lives next door.

Every day, after school, we play together.

My mother says that I can visit Aaron sometimes.

But it won't be the same.

We drove to our new house.

There were boxes everywhere.

I helped my mother and father unpack
some of the boxes.

Then I went outside to look at our new garden.

That is when I discovered...

... Max!
Now I have a new home,
and a new friend to play with as well.